RABBITS
FRENDS AND
RALETIONS

MY
HOUSE

OWLS
HOUSE

100 AKER

WOOD

EEYORES

First published in Great Britain 1999
by Methuen Children's Books
an imprint of Egmont Children's Books Limited
239 Kensington High Street, London W8 6SA

3 5 7 9 10 8 6 4 2

Printed in Belgium

ISBN 0 416 19639 X

THIS BOOK

BELONGS TO

· ·

THE
WINNIE-THE-POOH
ADDRESS
BOOK

A. A. Milne   E. H. Shepard

Methuen Children's Books

Essential Data for Organised Bears

Name

Address

Postcode

Telephone (home)

Telephone (work)

National Insurance number

Passport number

Driving Licence number

Car Registration

Breakdown Membership number

Car Insurance number

National Health number

Blood Group

Any Known Allergies

More Numbers to Remember

Dentist

Doctor

Cinema

Electrician

Gas

Insurance

Local Authority

Neighbour

Plumber

Police Station

Optician

Rail enquiries

Taxi

Telephone Engineer

"*Do you know what this is?*"

"*No,*" said Piglet.

"*It's an A.*"

"*Oh,*" said Piglet.

"*Not O – A,*" said Eeyore severely. "*Can't you hear, or do you think you have more education than Christopher Robin?*"

A

Name

Address

Telephone

Name

Address

Telephone

Name

Address

Telephone

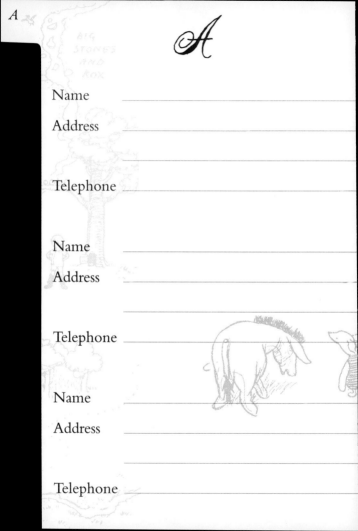

A

Name _____

Address _____

_____

Telephone _____

Name _____

Address _____

_____

Telephone _____

Name _____

Address _____

_____

Telephone _____

A

Name

Address

Telephone

Name

Address

Telephone

Name

Address

Telephone

"Now then, Pooh," said Christopher Robin, "where's your boat?"

"I ought to say," explained Pooh as they walked down to the shore of the island, "that it isn't just an ordinary sort of boat. Sometimes it's a Boat, and sometimes it's more of an Accident. It all depends."

"Depends on what?"

"On whether I'm on the top of it or underneath it."

Name

Address

Telephone

Name

Address

Telephone

Name

Address

Telephone

Name

Address

Telephone

Name

Address

Telephone

Name

Address

Telephone

Name

Address

Telephone

Name

Address

Telephone

Name

Address

Telephone

"Well," said Owl, "the customary procedure in such cases is as follows."

"What does Crustimoney Proseedcake mean?" said Pooh. "For I am a Bear of Very Little Brain, and long words Bother me."

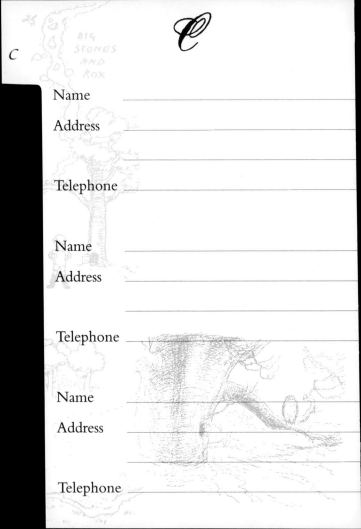

C

BIG
STONES
AND
ROX

Name

Address

Telephone

Name

Address

Telephone

Name

Address

Telephone

C

C

Name

Address

Telephone

Name

Address

Telephone

Name

Address

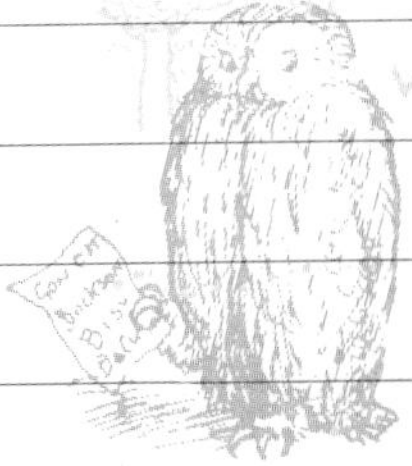

Telephone

C

BIG
STONES
AND
ROX

Name

Address

Telephone

Name

Address

Telephone

Name

Address

Telephone

The Old Grey Donkey, Eeyore, stood by himself in a thistly corner of the Forest, his front feet well apart, his head on one side, and thought about things. Sometimes he thought sadly to himself, "Why?" and sometimes he thought, "Wherefore?" and sometimes he thought, "Inasmuch as which?" – and sometimes he didn't quite know what he was thinking about.

Name

Address

Telephone

Name

Address

Telephone

Name

Address

Telephone

Name

Address

Telephone

Name

Address

Telephone

Name

Address

Telephone

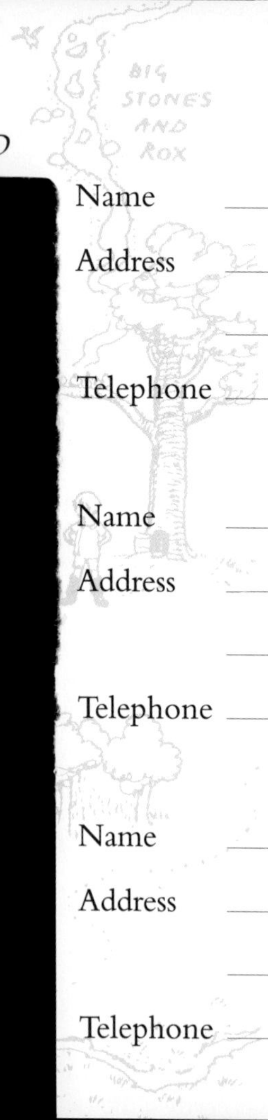

D

BIG
STONES
AND
ROX

Name

Address

Telephone

Name

Address

Telephone

Name

Address

Telephone

"*Thank you, Christopher Robin. You're the only one who seems to understand about tails. They don't think – that's what's the matter with some of these others. They've no imagination. A tail isn't a tail to them, it's just a Little Bit Extra at the back.*"

E

Name

Address

Telephone

Name

Address

Telephone

Name

Address

Telephone

Name _____

Address _____

_____

Telephone _____

Name _____

Address _____

_____

Telephone _____

Name _____

Address _____

_____

Telephone _____

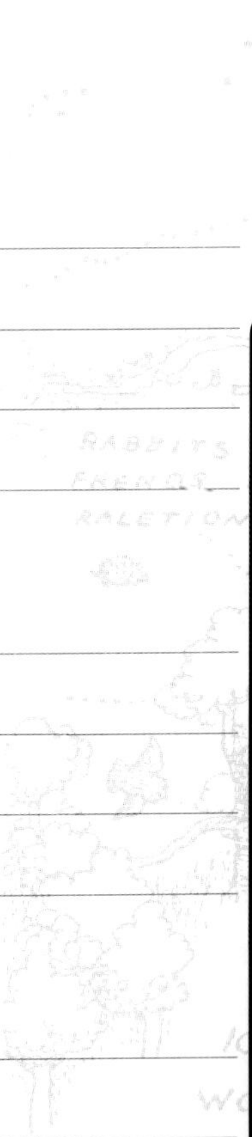

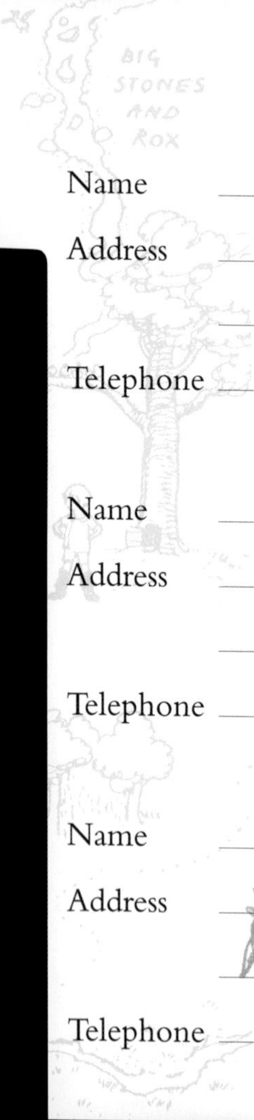

E

ℰ

Name

Address

Telephone

Name

Address

Telephone

Name

Address

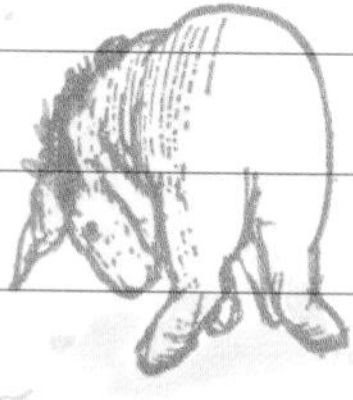

Telephone

. . . and when Christopher Robin had nailed it on in its right place again, Eeyore frisked about the forest, waving his tail so happily that Winnie-the-Pooh came over all funny, and had to hurry home for a little snack of something to sustain him.

F

Name

Address

Telephone

Name

Address

Telephone

Name

Address

Telephone

Name _____

Address _____

_____

Telephone _____

Name _____

Address _____

_____

Telephone _____

Name _____

Address _____

_____

Telephone _____

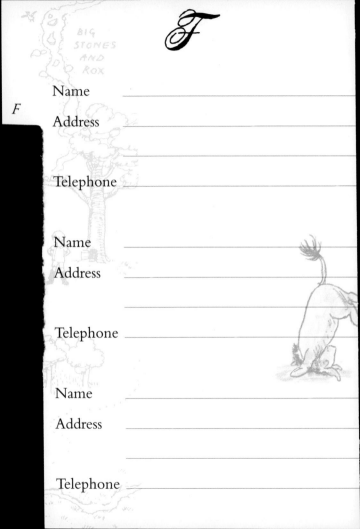

BIG
STONES
AND
ROX

Name _____

Address _____

_____

Telephone _____

Name _____

Address _____

_____

Telephone _____

Name _____

Address _____

_____

Telephone _____

"Good morning, Pooh
Bear," said Eeyore gloomily.
"If it is a good morning,"
he said. "Which I doubt,"
said he.

"Why,
what's the matter?"
"Nothing,
Pooh Bear, nothing.
We can't all, and some of us don't.
That's all there is to it."

Name

Address

Telephone

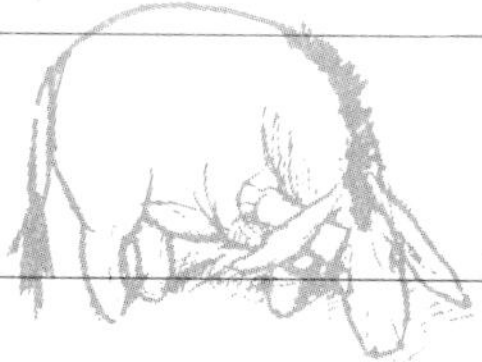

Name

Address

Telephone

Name

Address

Telephone

Name

Address

G

Telephone

Name

Address

Telephone

Name

Address

Telephone

$\mathcal{G}$

G

Name

Address

Telephone

Name

Address

Telephone

Name

Address

Telephone

Some hours later, just as the night was beginning to steal away, Pooh woke up suddenly with a sinking feeling. He had had that sinking feeling before, and he knew what it meant. HE WAS HUNGRY.

Name

Address

Telephone

Name

Address

Telephone

Name

Address

Telephone

Name

Address

Telephone

Name

Address

Telephone

Name

Address

Telephone

H

Name

Address

Telephone

Name

Address

Telephone

Name

Address

Telephone

"There is an Invitation for you."
"What's that like?"
"An Invitation!"
"Yes, I heard you. Who dropped it?"

J

Name

Address

Telephone

Name

Address

Telephone

Name

Address

Telephone

J

Name

Address

Telephone

Name

Address

Telephone

Name

Address

Telephone

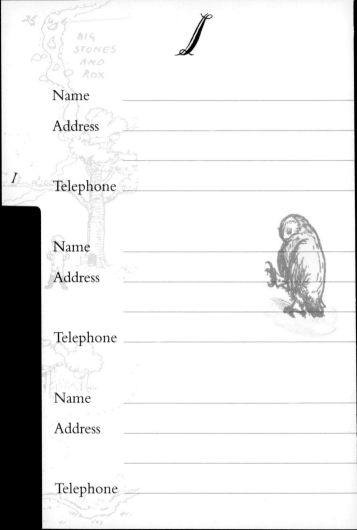

Name

Address

Telephone

Name

Address

Telephone

Name

Address

Telephone

"Is it One of the Fiercer Animals?" he said, looking the
other way.
Pooh nodded. "It's a Jagular," he said.
"What do Jagulars do?" asked Piglet, hoping that they
wouldn't.

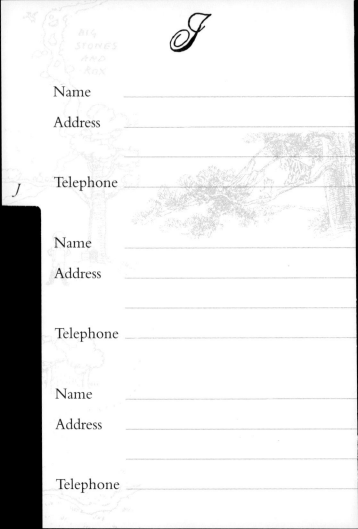

J

Name

Address

Telephone

Name

Address

Telephone

Name

Address

Telephone

Name

Address

Telephone

J

Name

Address

Telephone

Name

Address

Telephone

Name

Address

Telephone

Name

Address

Telephone

Name

Address

Telephone

K

"Is it a very Grand thing to be an
Afternoon, what you said?"
"A what?" said Christopher Robin
lazily, as he listened to something else.
"On a horse?" explained Pooh.
"A Knight?"
"Oh, was that it?" said Pooh.

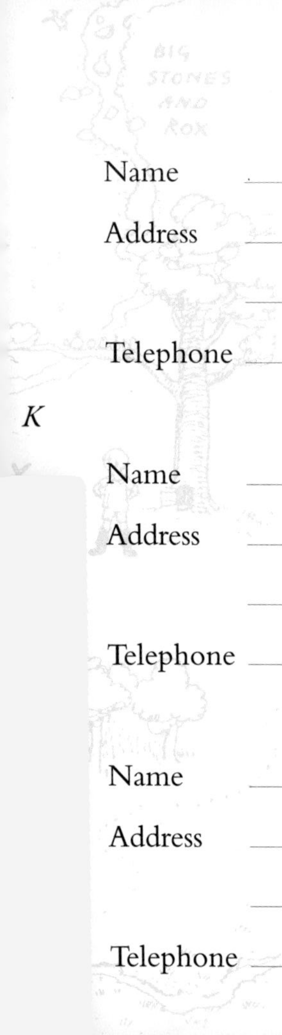

Name

Address

Telephone

K

Name

Address

Telephone

Name

Address

Telephone

Name

Address

Telephone

K

Name

Address

Telephone

Name

Address

Telephone

K

K

Name

Address

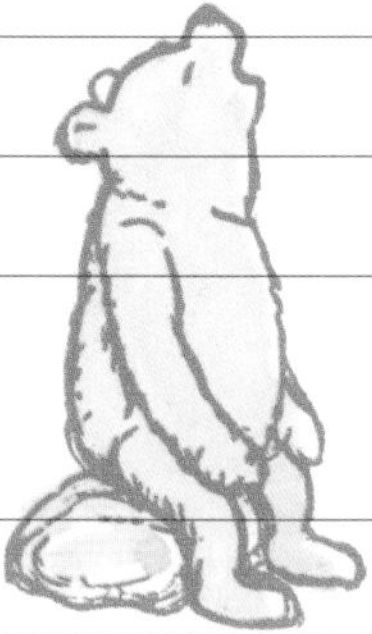

Telephone

Name

Address

Telephone

Name

Address

Telephone

"Oh, Bear!" said
Christopher Robin.
"How I do love you!"
"So do I," said Pooh.

L

Name

Address

Telephone

Name

Address

Telephone

Name

Address

Telephone

Name _____

Address _____

_____

Telephone _____

Name _____

Address _____

Telephone _____

Name _____

Address _____

_____

Telephone _____

L

Name

Address

Telephone

Name

Address

Telephone

Name

Address

Telephone

"It's a Missage," he said to himself, "that's what it is. And that letter is a 'P', and so is that, and so is that, and 'P' means 'Pooh', so it's a very important Missage to me, and I can't read it. I must find Christopher Robin or Owl or Piglet, one of those Clever Readers who can read things, and they will tell me what this message means . . .

Name

Address

Telephone

Name

Address

Telephone

Name

Address

Telephone

M

Name

Address

Telephone

Name

Address

Telephone

M

Name

Address

Telephone

M

Name _____

Address _____

_____

Telephone _____

Name _____

Address _____

_____

Telephone _____

Name _____

Address _____

_____

Telephone _____

"*How do you do Nothing?*" asked Pooh, after he had wondered for a long time.

"*Well, it's when people call out at you just as you're going off to do it, 'What are you going to do, Christopher Robin?' and you say 'Oh, nothing,' and then you go and do it.*"

"*Oh, I see,*" said Pooh.

Name

Address

Telephone

Name

Address

Telephone

Name

Address

Telephone

Name

Address

Telephone

Name

Address

Telephone

Name

Address

Telephone

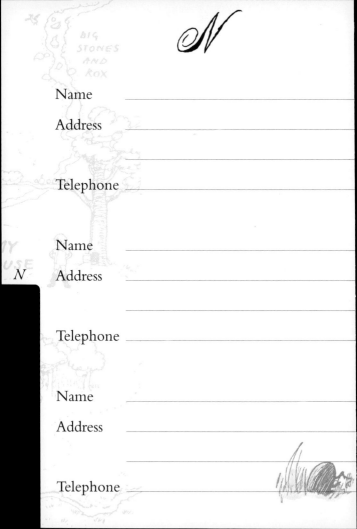

N

Name

Address

Telephone

Name

Address

Telephone

Name

Address

Telephone

"That's right. You'll like Owl. He flew past
a day or two ago and noticed me. He didn't
actually say anything, mind you, but he
knew it was me. Very friendly of him,
I thought. Encouraging."

Name

Address

Telephone

Name

Address

Telephone

Name

Address

Telephone

Name

Address

Telephone

Name

Address

O

Telephone

Name

Address

Telephone

O

Name _____

Address _____

_____

Telephone _____

Name _____

Address _____

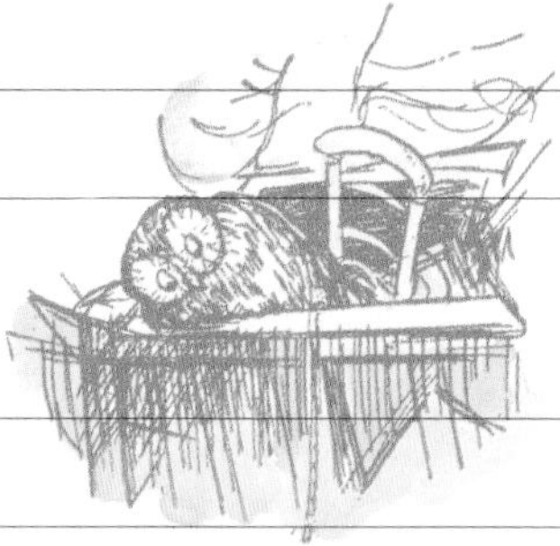

_____

Telephone _____

Name _____

Address _____

_____

Telephone _____

"...And we must all
bring Provisions."
"Bring what?"
"Things to eat."

Name

Address

Telephone

Name

Address

Telephone

Name

Address

Telephone

Name

Address

Telephone

Name

Address

Telephone

Name

Address

Telephone

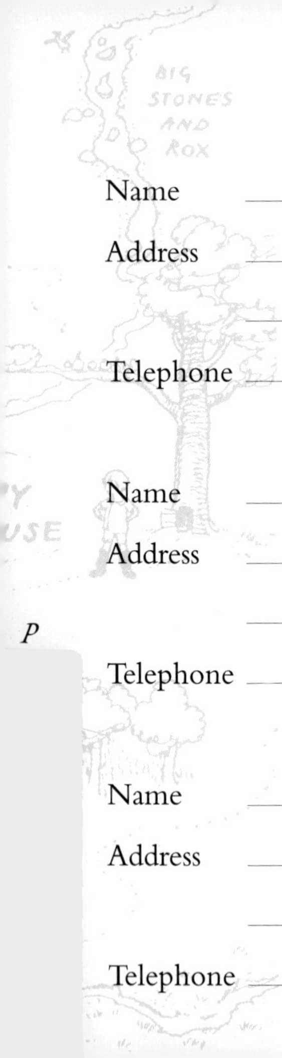

Name

Address

Telephone

Name

Address

Telephone

Name

Address

Telephone

...Tigger, who had been hiding behind trees and jumping out on Pooh's shadow when it wasn't looking, said that Tiggers were only bouncy before breakfast, and that as soon as they had had a few haycorns they became Quiet and Refined.

Name

Address

Telephone

Name

Address

Q Telephone

Name

Address

Telephone

Name

Address

Telephone

Name

Address

Telephone

Q

Name

Address

Telephone

BIG
STONES
AND
ROX

Name

Address

Telephone

Name

Address

Telephone

Name

Address

Telephone

"Who is Small?"

"One of my friends-and-relations," said Rabbit carelessly.
This didn't help Pooh much, because Rabbit had so many
friends-and-relations, and of such different sorts and sizes,
that he didn't know whether he ought to be looking for Small
at the top of an oak-tree or in the petal of a buttercup.

Name

Address

Telephone

Name

Address

Telephone

R

Name

Address

Telephone

Name

Address

Telephone

Name

Address

Telephone

Name

Address

Telephone

R

R

Name

Address

Telephone

Name

Address

Telephone

R

Name

Address

Telephone

"If anybody wants to clap," said Eeyore . . .
"now is the time to do it."
They all clapped.
"Thank you," said Eeyore. "Unexpected
and gratifying, if a little lacking in Smack."

Name

Address

Telephone

Name

Address

Telephone

S

Name

Address

Telephone

Name

Address

Telephone

Name

Address

Telephone

S

Name

Address

Telephone

Name

Address

Telephone

Name

Address

Telephone

Name

Address

Telephone

Half-way between Pooh's house and Piglet's house was a Thoughtful Spot where they met sometimes when they had decided to go and see each other, and as it was warm and out of the wind they would sit down there for a little and wonder what they would do now that they had seen each other.

Name

Address

Telephone

Name

Address

Telephone

T

Name

Address

Telephone

Name

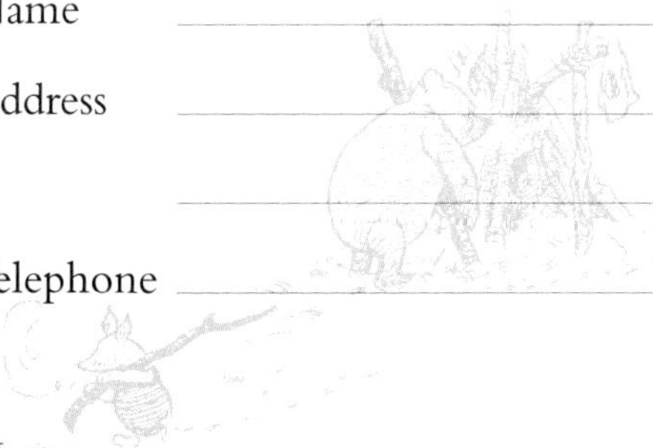

Address

Telephone

Name

Address

Telephone

Name

Address

Telephone

T

Name

Address

Telephone

Name

Address

Telephone

T Name

Address

Telephone

"It's Piglet!" cried Pooh
eagerly. "Where are you?"
"Underneath," said Piglet
in an underneath sort of way.
"Underneath what?"
"You," squeaked Piglet. "Get up!"

U

Name

Address

Telephone

Name

Address

Telephone

Name

Address

Telephone

U

U

Name

Address

Telephone

Name

Address

Telephone

Name

Address

Telephone

U

U

Name

Address

Telephone

Name

Address

Telephone

Name

Address

Telephone

WHERE SHOULD THEY DIG THE VERY DEEP PIT?
Piglet said that the best place would be somewhere where a
Heffalump was, just before he fell into it, only about a foot
further on.

Name

Address

Telephone

Name

Address

Telephone

Name

Address

V

Telephone

Name

Address

Telephone

Name

Address

Telephone

Name

Address

Telephone

V

Name

Address

Telephone

Name

Address

Telephone

Name

Address

Telephone

V

*He could spell his own name WOL, and he could spell
Tuesday so that you knew it wasn't Wednesday, and he could
read quite comfortably when you weren't looking over his
shoulder and saying "Well?" all the time . . .*

Name

Address

Telephone

Name

Address

Telephone

Name

Address

W

Telephone

Name

Address

Telephone

Name

Address

Telephone

Name

Address

W

Telephone

WOL

Name

Address

Telephone

Name

Address

Telephone

Name

Address

W

Telephone

"We are all going on an Expedition," said Christopher Robin, as he got up and brushed himself. "Thank you, Pooh."
"Going on an Expotition?" said Pooh eagerly. "I don't think I've ever been on one of those. Where are we going to on this Expotition?"
"Expedition, silly old Bear. It's got an 'x' in it."

Name

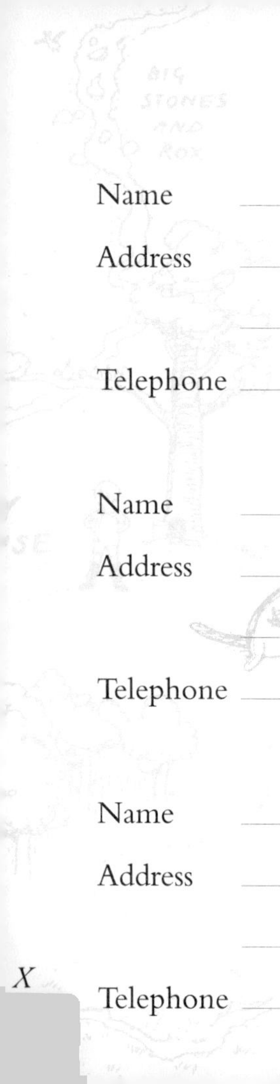

Address

Telephone

Name

Address

Telephone

Name

Address

X   Telephone

Name

Address

Telephone

Name

Address

Telephone

Name

Address

Telephone

Name

Address

Telephone

Name

Address

Telephone

Name

Address

X Telephone

"I might have known," said Eeyore. "After all, one can't complain. I have my friends. Somebody spoke to me only yesterday. And was it last week or the week before that Rabbit bumped into me and said 'Bother!' The Social Round. Always something going on."

Y
Z

Name

Address

Telephone

Name

Address

Telephone

Name

Address

Telephone

Y

Name

Address

Telephone

Name

Address

Telephone

Name

Address

Telephone

Name

Address

Telephone

Name

Address

Telephone

Name

Address

Telephone

Y

"That buzzing-noise means something.
You don't get a buzzing-noise like
that, just buzzing and buzzing,
without its meaning something. If
there's a buzzing-noise, somebody's
making a buzzing-noise, and the only
reason for making a buzzing-noise that
I know of is because you're a bee . . .

. . . And the only
reason for being a
bee that I know of is
making honey . . ."

Z

Z

Name

Address

Telephone

Name

Address

Telephone

Name

Address

Telephone

Name

Address

Telephone

Name

Address

Telephone

Name

Address

Telephone

Z

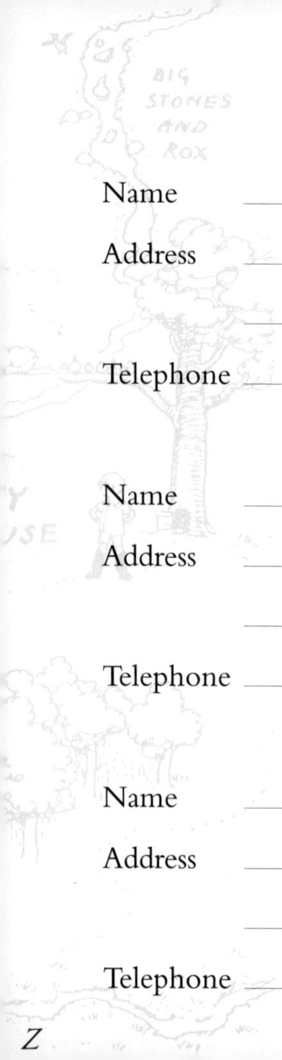

Name _____

Address _____

_____

_____

Telephone _____

Name _____

Address _____

_____

Telephone _____

Name _____

Address _____

_____

Telephone _____

Z

Name

Address

Telephone

Name

Address

Telephone

Name

Address

Telephone

Z

More friends-and-relations

Name

Address

Telephone

Name

Address

Telephone

Name

Address

Telephone

More friends-and-relations

Name

Address

Telephone

Name

Address

Telephone

Name

Address

Telephone

More friends-and-relations

Name

Address

Telephone

Name

Address

Telephone

Name

Address

Telephone

More friends-and-relations

Name

Address

Telephone

Name

Address

Telephone

Name

Address

Telephone

More friends-and-relations

Name

Address

Telephone

Name

Address

Telephone

Name

Address

Telephone

More friends-and-relations

Name _____

Address _____

_____

Telephone _____

Name _____

Address _____

_____

Telephone _____

Name _____

Address _____

_____

Telephone _____

Birthdays

Birthdays

Birthdays

Birthdays

PIKNIC

KANGAS
HOUSE

SANDY PIT
WHERE ROO PLAYS

RABBITS
HOUSE

POOH BEARS
HOUSE

SIX PINE
TREES.

POOH TRAP FOR
HEFFALUMPS

PIGLETS
HOUSE

O

H